Our Emotions and Behaviour

I Want to Win!

Written by Sue Graves

Illustrated by
Emanuela Carletti and
Desideria Guicciardini

W
FRANKLIN WATTS
LONDON • SYDNEY

In the holidays, Bella went to Fun Club. Nell and Matt were the club leaders. They always thought of exciting things for everyone to do.

There were board games and floor games. There were quizzes and puzzles.

There were things to make and bake and paint.

But Bella always wanted to be **the best.** She wanted to win everything.

If she didn't win, she **got cross.**

Matt said winning wasn't important.
He said it was important to **try hard**
and to be a **good sport**.

But Bella didn't listen. She didn't want to be a good sport ever!

One day, Nell and Matt had a **big surprise.** They said everyone was going to build a den. The best den would win a **prize.**

Everyone built a den. Most of the children **tried their best.** But Bella said it was **too hard** to build a den.

Bella stopped trying.

She got cross and **gave up**.
Nell went to talk to her.

Nell said everyone finds some things hard to do. She said she couldn't ride a bike when she was little. She kept wobbling and falling off. But she didn't give up. She kept trying. Soon she could ride really well.

Bella had a good think. She said she would **try hard** to build a den. She said she wouldn't give up until it was finished.

Bella did her best to build a den.

She tried again...

...and again...

...and again.

20

At last the den was finished. It looked a bit odd but Bella was proud of herself anyway. She was pleased she had finished it.

Then everyone voted for the best den.
Matt counted all the votes.

Everyone voted for Charlie's den. It was brilliant!
Bella **felt happy** for Charlie.

Then Matt told everyone that he had another prize – for the person who had **tried the hardest**. He said that **Bella** had tried the hardest, and that she was a good sport, too.

Bella said being **a good sport** was much nicer than getting cross. She said it was more fun, too.

Everyone agreed!

Can you tell the story of what happens when the class has a competition to grow the tallest sunflower?

How do you think Billy felt when his sunflower didn't win? How did he feel when they all made a display?

A note about sharing this book

The *Our Emotions and Behaviour* series has been developed to provide a starting point for further discussion on children's feelings and behaviour, both in relation to themselves and to other people.

I Want to Win!
This story looks at the importance of trying hard and being a good sport. It examines the problems that can arise when people find it hard to cope with disappointment or when they find it difficult to achieve ambitions. It takes the opportunity to look at ways to overcome difficulties – and reminds us never to give up!

Storyboard puzzle
The wordless storyboard on pages 26 and 27 provides an opportunity for speaking and listening. Children are encouraged to tell the story illustrated in the panels: the class mates are excited about the competition to grow the tallest sunflower. They each plant some seeds. They each water their plants carefully. Billy's sunflower, however, does not grow as tall as the other children's. He is getting more and more frustrated and he is really cross when he doesn't win. Then he sees all the sunflowers making a display and is pleased he made the effort to grow one after all.

How to use the book
The book is designed for adults to share with either an individual child or a group of children, and as a starting point for discussion.

The book also provides visual support and repeated words and phrases to build confidence in children who are starting to read on their own.

Before reading the story
Choose a time to read when you and the children are relaxed and have time to share the story.

Spend time looking at the illustrations and talk about what the book may be about before reading it together.

28

After reading, talk about the book with the children:

- What was it about? Have the children ever felt cross because they have not won something or because they found something hard to do?

- Have they ever given up if something proves too difficult to do? What things do they find hard? Does everyone find the same things hard or do different people find different things difficult?

- Ask the children to recall instances when they tried hard to achieve something. How did they feel if they succeeded? How did they feel if they tried hard and did not succeed? Conversely, how did they feel if they gave up without really trying?

Ask the children why they think it is important to be a good sport. Ask them to recount events from their own experiences when they had to be good sports about something.

To Isabelle, William A, George, William G, Max,
Emily, Leo, Caspar, Felix and Phoebe –S.G.

Franklin Watts
First published in Great Britain in 2017 by The Watts Publishing Group

Text © Franklin Watts 2017
Illustrations © Emanuela Carletti and Desideria Guicciardini 2017

ISBN (hardback) 978 1 4451 5198 4
ISBN (paperback) 978 1 4451 5199 1

Editor: Jackie Hamley
Designer: Peter Scoulding

Printed in China

Franklin Watts
An imprint of
Hachette Children's Group
Part of The Watts Publishing Group
Carmelite House
50 Victoria Embankment
London EC4Y 0DZ

An Hachette UK Company
www.hachette.co.uk

www.franklinwatts.co.uk